'No five o'clock on our calendars'
A history of hay time in the North Pennines

Edited by Rebecca Barrett and Neil Diment

Contents

Front cover:
Grandma Freda, Auntie Dora and a very young Bernard Hooper pose with a horse-drawn hay sweep at Brockersgill Farm, Newbiggin-in-Teesdale in the late 1930s.

Inside front cover:
A hay time group at Breckholm Farm near Middleton-in-Teesdale, c.1910. As former County Durham Antiquities Officer Dennis Coggins has written, in those days 'everyone, from the oldest to the youngest, was expected to turn out to help while neighbours and visiting relatives were always sure of a welcome'.

Title Page:
Paddy-sweeping hay, Bowes, 1930s.

Foreword

Richard Betton
Upper Teesdale Agricultural Support Service and member of the Hay Time – North Pennines project steering group

Haymaking has and always will be hard work. This book captures the evolution of this age-old process from horse-drawn mowers to the invention of the big bale silage and haylage techniques which have made such a huge difference, not only enabling a reasonable quality winter feed to be made in moderate summers, but also eradicating the scourge of "Farmers' Lung". Improved technology has also allowed the ever-dwindling farming population to continue the traditional management practices, albeit with modern equipment, that are responsible for the maintenance of the renowned flower-rich meadows of the North Pennines created by their predecessors.

Richard Betton amid globeflowers on his farm at Harwood-in-Teesdale.

As a farmer myself, having led and stacked bales through most of the night, there is nothing more gratifying than being woken up the next morning by the sound of rain lashing against the bedroom window (rain in Harwood in Upper Teesdale tends to be horizontal) knowing that all is safely (and dryly) gathered in. The old farming saying that "a mow full of hay is as good as money in the bank" is based on sound fact: over the years farming businesses have thrived, survived or died on the results of one hay time.

In the early 18th century George I described an English summer as "two fine days followed by a thunderstorm" and that was describing the weather in the south! This book celebrates the achievements of the farming population in an area of significant natural handicaps (harsh winters, low temperatures, high rainfall and poor soils). It is also an overdue recognition of the dedication, knowledge and skills that have for too long not been acknowledged or have been taken for granted by policy makers and some of the regulatory bodies. It will strike a cord with everyone who reads it: not just with visitors to the North Pennines but especially with all older farmers and remind them of the times they have frantically worked in the hay field with one eye on approaching black clouds heralding an imminent thunderstorm or "precipitation within sight" as they say on the Shipping Forecast.

The North Pennines Area of Outstanding Natural Beauty

Chris Woodley-Stewart, Director, North Pennines AONB Partnership

'This country, though politically distributed among three counties, is one and the same in all its characteristic features. From it flow the Tyne, the Wear and the Tees and many branches which fall into these rivers. Along the banks of these and several other smaller streams which fall into them are dales or valleys, cultivated near the banks and for a short distance up the sides of the hills, but soon cultivation and enclosure cease, and beyond them the dark fells, covered with peat and moss and heath; and between one vale and another is a wide extent of high moorland, extending sometimes for a dozen miles. In these upland tracts are no inhabited homes but thousands of blackfaced sheep are scattered over them.'

(Royal Commission into Children's Employment in the Mines, W.R. Mitchell, 1842)

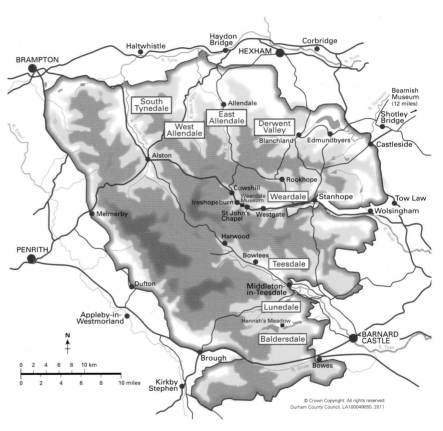

© Crown Copyright. All rights reserved
Durham County Council. LA100049055. 2011

This description of the North Pennines from 1842 might equally have been written today, but it would be misleading to consider the North Pennines landscape as timeless and unchanging. The march of time has brought many changes in where and how people live and how the landscape is managed; its relative 'wildness' has been very much shaped by people over several thousand years. Nowhere has this human intervention been more obviously beneficial to nature than in our species-rich upland hay meadows. Here the needs of the farmer and the needs of nature can combine to create something truly special – meadows awash with wildflowers, alive with insects and birds.

But these meadows are not just a natural treasure, they are a cultural gem too. The changes in agriculture and society in the last 60 or so years have brought about enormous changes in our hay meadows and how they are managed. In these pages you'll see how 'hay time' has changed over the years, finding out about it at first hand from those that have been there in the fields, often alongside their families, friends and neighbours. It is a wonderful journey, through a fascinating aspect of a very special place - the North Pennines.

The North Pennines AONB was designated in 1988. One of the most remote and unspoilt places in England, it straddles the boundaries of County Durham, Cumbria and Northumberland. As well as having 40% of the UK's species-rich upland hay meadows, it is a place of wild open moorlands, tumbling rivers, rich birdlife and history of human occupation and culture stretching back 7000 years.

The Hay Time meadow restoration project

Rebecca Barrett, North Pennines AONB Partnership

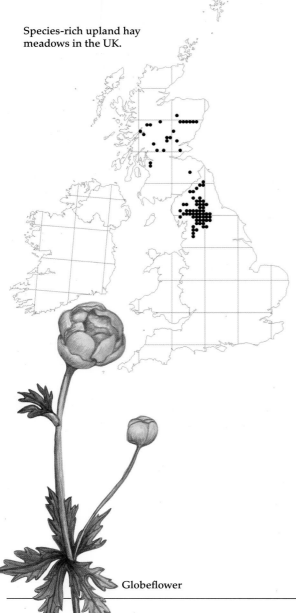

Species-rich upland hay meadows in the UK.

Globeflower

Within the UK, species-rich hay meadows are a rare habitat, having declined by more than 97% over the past 60 years as a result of progressive agricultural intensification. The meadows found in the North Pennines are a special type, characteristic of the harsh conditions typical of hilly and mountainous regions across Europe. These 'upland' or 'mountain' hay meadows are now a very rare habitat with little more than 900ha thought to remain in the UK. With 350ha of upland hay meadows, the North Pennines AONB is an important place for this special habitat.

From a botanical perspective, the importance of upland hay meadows lies in the rich diversity of wild plants that grow in them. The best meadows can support up to 120 different species of flowering plant. Many of these are characteristic of northern latitudes and are found close to their southern boundary in the North Pennines, species like *wood crane's-bill, melancholy thistle* and *globeflower*, for example.

Farmers in the North Pennines have been able to claim financial incentives for managing their hay meadows non-intensively since the 1980s. However, at the turn of the 21st century, even where traditional management practices had been restored to meadows which had lost their special species, there was little evidence of their return and many meadows continued to decline in quality. The limited potential for seeds to migrate naturally from neighbouring fields due to the rarity and highly fragmented nature of species-rich meadows is an important factor in this.

The process of natural seed migration can be speeded-up significantly by the direct addition of seed that has been harvested from nearby species-rich meadows. This approach has been experimentally and practically demonstrated and seed addition is now a recognised and increasingly used technique for grassland restoration. Experimental work has also shown that the seeds of different species should be introduced at different stages of the meadow restoration process. At the first stage

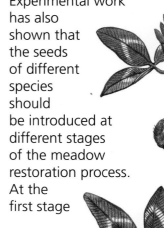

Red clover

species such as *yellow rattle*, *red clover*, *sweet vernal grass* and *meadow buttercup* should be introduced as these plants encourage changes in the soil so that they are suitable for more specialised meadow plants to colonise. The second stage of the restoration process is to introduce species associated with classic upland hay meadows, such as *wood crane's-bill* and *globeflower*, although it may take a number of years before soil conditions change sufficiently to enable a diverse vegetation to flourish. *Yellow rattle* is a particularly important plant in the meadow restoration process as it parasitizes and weakens grasses, thus creating patches of bare soil where other species can establish.

Since May 2006, the North Pennines AONB Partnership has been working closely with farmers and with Natural England to restore meadows that have lost their characteristic plant species through our project, 'Hay Time'. Using special machinery, we harvest either the seed-bearing top of the hay crop or the entire crop and then spread it as 'green hay' on a nearby meadow. Not only does this approach enable the effective transfer of seeds, a process that would take decades to occur naturally, but it ensures that the unique genetic integrity of these meadows is maintained.

Species-rich hay meadow in Upper Teesdale, July 2010.

Harvesting species-rich green hay, Weardale, August 2007.

Harvesting the 'top of the hay', Allendale, August 2009.

Meadow buttercup

Spreading hay meadow seed in green hay, Upper Teesdale, August 2010.

Harvested green hay full of yellow rattle seed.

The AONB Partnership's Hay Time project officer, Ruth Starr-Keddle, surveying.

Sadly some of the most special upland hay meadow plants are now becoming so scarce that in some areas they are not abundant enough for us to harvest them using machinery. In these areas we have enlisted the help of volunteers to gather seed by hand from species-rich banks and roadside verges. These have been either spread directly onto the meadows or been grown-on over one or two years until the young plants are robust enough to be planted out.

Careful scientific baseline and monitoring surveys underlie our work. Effective restoration of natural habitats is a process that takes years and often decades to achieve. The management and restoration of hay meadows is particularly complicated because it depends on continual and appropriate human intervention. We address these issues by working on meadows that are subject to ten year management agreements under the terms of agri-environment schemes such as the Higher Level Scheme of Environmental Stewardship.

People are fundamental to the future of our meadows. Upland hay meadows depend upon an annual cycle of farm management. If this were to cease, the characteristic flowers of the meadows would soon disappear and with them a spectrum of birds and insects. Helping farmers to manage their meadows in ways that will benefit biodiversity, and providing them with a practical mechanism to restore their meadows, are important tasks if our meadow heritage is to have a bright future.

Yellow rattle

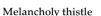

Melancholy thistle

'Ask the Fellows who Cut the Hay'

Traditional hay meadow management in the North Pennines

Neil Diment, North Pennines AONB Partnership

From a different line of work, my colleagues,
I bring you an idea. You smirk.
It's in the line of duty. Wipe off that smile, and
As our grandfather's used to say:
Ask the fellows who cut the hay.

(from The Decade of Sheng Min, translated by Ezra Pound)

George Ewart Evans is acknowledged as having written the pioneering oral history book in the UK. It took its title from a line in Ezra Pound's translation – although, ironically, haymaking is barely mentioned in the stories of rural life he collected from the arable lowlands of East Suffolk over half a century ago.

In 2006, the North Pennines AONB Partnership launched its own historical research project to explore the history of hay time in the area. This book, and much else besides, was gleaned from that work. We did indeed not only 'ask the fellows who cut the hay' – but those who turned and strewed, raked and rowed, piked and led it too!*

One thing that quickly emerged was the fact that, while many tools and artefacts – the 'hardware' of hay time – still survived, albeit much of it neglected and rusting in the corners of farmyards and fields, the memories and stories of hay time were fast disappearing. Very little had been written about hay time, but those stories still survived, just, within living memory. These are stories of ordinary people doing what many today, in a largely urban population, must view as extraordinary things. They are stories of a time, after the Second World War and even into the early 1960s, where haytiming still carried on in the upper dales with horses and hand rakes pretty much as it had done for centuries. Many of these 'old haytimers' were happy to share their stories with us. Some were pleased, some mildly surprised that anyone should care to listen, still less want to record those stories for posterity. This book is a small attempt to honour the results of generation upon generation of labour, recognising and capturing those hay time traditions before they're gone forever.

The 1960s saw the advent of the 'little grey Fergie' and other early tractors; horses were literally put out to grass and hand rakes hung up on barn walls for perhaps the last time. The old, slow, weather-dependent ways soon went as farmers were urged to increase production and intensify their farming. Old meadows were reseeded to become 'improved grassland'. Artificial fertilisers were used to increase yields. After early experiments in the 50s, silage-making gained in popularity, since good quality fodder could be won whatever the weather.

An old Nicholson horse-drawn hay rake, left abandoned on a roadside verge in Allendale.

* For readers unfamiliar with any of these hay time terms, please see the glossary on p. 34 & 35.

Sign of things to come.
A cheerful-looking Arthur Dowson baling hay in Beck Head meadow on Howe Farm, Kelton, in Lunedale, in the early 1960s. He's driving a Massey Ferguson 35 pulling a McCormick International Baler.

Hay time was one of the most important times of year in the farmer's calendar. If he didn't get enough hay in to feed his livestock – typically dairy Shorthorn cattle and Swaledale sheep – over the winter when nothing else grew, they would go hungry; and with no livestock to sell at market the following year, so might he and his family. In those days there was no animal feed to buy in and very little spare money to do so even if there had been. Farmers needed four consecutive sunny days to make hay – one to mow the grass, one to turn and strew it, one to row it up and one to lead it into the barn or field house – and you rarely get that in the North Pennines.

It was an anxious time, totally dependent on the weather, and no-one could relax until the hay was won. No wonder there was rarely any celebration or supper at the end of it, unlike harvest time in the lowlands. Everyone was just too tired. And if you were lucky enough to get yours in, you went and helped your neighbours get theirs. The whole family worked long, long days; friends and neighbours were roped in to help and any relatives living in nearby towns might be encouraged to travel up to the farm for a 'holiday'!

Hay time through the centuries

It is likely that the origins of some of the hay meadows in the North Pennines date back to the activities of early Bronze Age farmers 4,000 years ago, who would have been faced with the same problem of providing winter feed for their stock as farmers are today. Some of the best land, certainly that nearest to the homesteads in the woodland clearings, was probably reserved as meadowland rather than being used for arable crop production.

Though rulers and landowners changed through the centuries, the farming year stayed much the same – at least as far as the meadows were concerned. The replacement of the sickle by the scythe by the 17th century allowed the reaper to stand rather

From past to present: a hay meadow time line

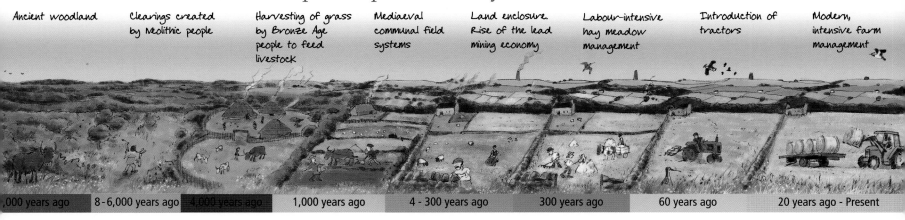

Ancient woodland | Clearings created by Neolithic people | Harvesting of grass by Bronze Age people to feed livestock | Mediaeval communal field systems | Land enclosure. Rise of the lead mining economy | Labour-intensive hay meadow management | Introduction of tractors | Modern, intensive farm management

,000 years ago | 8 - 6,000 years ago | 4,000 years ago | 1,000 years ago | 4 - 300 years ago | 300 years ago | 60 years ago | 20 years ago - Present

than stoop and must have eased those aching backs, though not much of the hard labour involved. The Victorians, with their inventions of horse-drawn machinery, paved the way for change, though the marginal uplands of the North Pennines may have been one of the last places in England to see the introduction of the single-bar cutter and horse rake.

The Teesdale Mercury,
January 13th 1864.

Grass-cutting Machine.

MR. W. SMITH, Whitesmith, of Barnard Castle, has obtained the Government Register for the protection of his improvements in his grass-cutting machine. Several of them have been already on trial and they seem to supply all the wants which have been so long a drawback to their more extensive use. He has succeeded in preventing the choking of the knives in a manner that contributes also to the strength of the Finger bar or without diminishing the strength of the Fingers. He has also invented a joint for the Finger bar that enables the machine to conform to the inequalities of the ground with perfect security, and his method of lightening the draught for the horses is not the least commendable part of his improvements. He has likewise improved several of the fittings, and has overcome all the difficulties which have so long been a drawback to the efficacy of so useful a piece of machinery. The agriculturists of this district will no doubt find it convenient to have an establishment in their own neighbourhood that can turn out as excellent a machine as this has proved itself to be, and Mr Smith may no doubt look forward to a good share of patronage.

In Teesdale, William Smith was quick to see that the new horse-drawn reapers imported from the United States for cutting wheat and oats could be adapted for cutting grass. He took out patents on his improvements and advertised his new machines with some success before concentrating on the production and sale of presumably more lucrative street-sweeping equipment, selling his stock of agricultural machinery to Bamfords of Uttoxeter, Staffordshire.

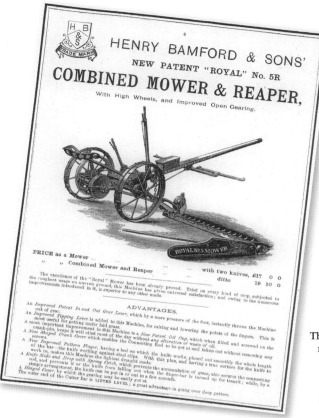

The machine that made Bamfords famous: the 'Royal' horse-drawn mower first introduced in 1882.

In the upper dales some of the meadows came into existence much later than those lower down – not until the late 18th to early 19th century boom in lead mining when a dual miner-farmer economy prevailed. The major lead mining businesses encouraged mining families to take small farms to ensure they had a stable workforce to exploit the mineral riches beneath the soil – and thus, perhaps, to persuade them to stay even when times were hard as the price of lead regularly rose and fell.

While the man of the household would be away from home for the working week, toiling by day in the mines and sleeping by night in the disease-ridden 'mineshop', his wife and children would be at home tending their smallholding, looking after their crops and a few animals – a cow, a pig, a few chickens – and all the time increasing the size of their middens! These provided valuable manure to fertilise the meadows to ensure that they would grow enough grass to feed their livestock over winter.

The haymaking year

Until mechanisation, meadows had seen little change in their management since Victorian days and even today the farming year still follows a similar pattern. There was though, no single pattern that every farmer followed. Each differed slightly according to individual custom and preference and other factors. He had no control over the steepness or the altitude of his fields. The higher up the dale, the later hay time could start. With increasing altitude, temperatures are a couple of degrees lower and the growing season correspondingly shorter.

For the hill farmer, the year starts in October when the lambs are sold at market. The rest of his flock are returned to his 'allotments' next to the moor. The meadows get a bit of a rest. Come the turning of the year and frosty weather, the well-rotted farmyard manure would be led out by horse and cart, and spread with forks.

Later on the fields might be harrowed to spread out the manure and break up any molehills – to keep the soil out of the hay and provide a more level surface for those early mowers so their cutter bars wouldn't get clogged up. Sheep would be allowed into the meadows to lamb in the spring, but once the lambs were old enough they would be removed and the meadow 'shut up' – typically in April to early May.

What's in a name?

What is a plant with a name like 'wood crane's-bill' (seen here) doing growing in a meadow? Its name perhaps gives a clue to the origins of many of our modern-day meadows – they were once clearings in the native woodland that covered much of this area before humans arrived. Its natural life cycle as an early-flowering woodland plant, when it would need to flower and seed before the canopy had closed overhead and shut out the sun, wouldn't be too dissimilar to that of the human-created habitat of the meadow, where again in order to survive it needs to flower and set its seed early before the farmer comes along with his scythe or mower.

The hay farming year

September–October	November	December–March	early March	early March	mid May	July–August
Lambs being fattened sell at market	Tups (male sheep) out with the ewes	Meadows left clear	Lambing starts. Some meadows grazed by ewes with lambs	Muck spreading, rolling and harrowing — Farmyard manure is the only fertiliser used on the best flower meadows — Harrowing evens out clumps	Lambing ends. All meadows clear of stock to allow the hay crop to grow	Hay (or silage) cut and baled. Cattle put in to graze for a week or so, then meadows are 'shut up' for a few weeks to allow the grass to grow

Autumn   Winter   Spring   Summer

For six weeks or so a transformation would then come over the meadows as the grasses and flowers burst into colour and life. The yellow of the early meadow buttercups would tend to be replaced by the magenta of the wood crane's-bill and, if the meadows were not cut until late August, the blood-red of great burnet followed. Bumblebees and other insects would be busy gathering nectar. Birds and other animals would be feeding and nesting.

> We never really thought about it, but like this field in front of here, we have all sorts of flowers in there. Sometimes early on it's yellow with buttercups, and then it turns blue with crane's-bills and there's a big patch of meadowsweet, and harebells, and melancholy thistles, oh, there is — and vetches. So there is a big variety of flowers. When we went to school, you see, we used to have to pick these flowers, and press them, and we had to know what they were. We could get a collection of flowers walking up the road side to school.

Des Collinson

Farmers liked the guarantee of an early June crop of hay if they could; it was better to get some feed in than let good haymaking weather pass by. If it was a poor summer though, getting the hay dry and into the barns could drag on well into September. Once the barns had been filled and the stacks made, and even the edges of the dry stone walled fields hacked back with a scythe – nothing was wasted, it was far too valuable – the grass would be allowed to grow for a couple of weeks. First the cattle and then the sheep would be brought back into the meadow to graze the aftermath or 'fog'. The lambs would be fattened for market, and the farming year would have turned once more.

Traditional meadows

Hay meadows have evolved through people repeating the same farm management over millennia in some cases. If one thing changes – the human management, or a natural factor like the climate – this will inevitably have an impact on the sward.

The photographs and quotes that follow in these pages illustrate and bring to life this yearly cycle and human struggle – a way of life, simpler and more dictated by the seasons perhaps, but physically much, much harder than today.

The quotes are taken from interviews undertaken in 2006/7 as part of a research project into the history of hay time in the North Pennines. They cover the period from the 1930s up to the early 1960s.

Meadow Memories
Hay time in words and pictures

The two most important things in the farming life... lambing time and hay time. And if you have good weather for both, if both goes well, you're lucky. But those are two important things, your lambs are going to be your income and your hay, feed for your animals.

Hannah Hauxwell

Oh, I dreaded hay times, I really did!

Des Collinson

Hay time, the process of winning hay, falls into three stages – mowing, haymaking and leading. But before it could begin there was much preparation to do. There was manuring and harrowing – and in some years spreading lime to sweeten the soil and basic slag to add more phosphorous:

Lime and slag seemed to go together. We wouldn't slag it every year, it'd be limed every year but it would be slagged maybe every five or six... and you could really tell where you'd been, you know, if you didn't put anything else on it, it grew a quite good sward...

Alan Scott

Then the meadows could be 'shut up':

The hay meadows would be shut up and allowed to grow... from mid-April to mid-May, somewhere around there, about the end of April I would say, on average. It depended on the season a lot, what the year was like, and the ewes and lambs were put back to the moor.

Alan Scott

John 'Ridley' Nevin shearing at Parkside Farm, Allendale, 1940s.

Often the start of hay time would immediately follow clipping time – one of the big social events in the farming year:

And all the old men used to come and they might clip two a day, and they would sit and talk the rest of the time. It was a social occasion, aye, and there was probably 20 of them.

Alan Scott

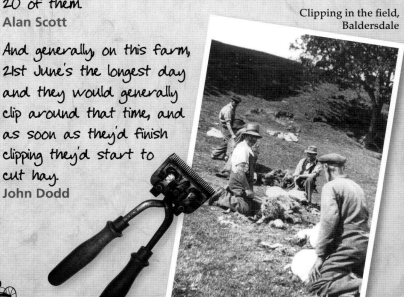

Clipping in the field, Baldersdale

And generally on this farm, 21st June's the longest day and they would generally clip around that time, and as soon as they'd finish clipping they'd start to cut hay.

John Dodd

'They had a hard life, had a horse.'

Then hay time could begin – but first you had to catch your horse! As a young lad Des Collinson recalls hay time could take all your summer holidays and…

Jim White's horse 'Bonnie' pulling an Albion grass cutter at The Rigg, Lunedale.

Before you went to school you probably had the horse to catch. Well, they're quite tall, and I wasn't big then.

And on a sunny day, it was always right at the top – on that steep pasture against the top wall. Now when it was a misty old day, when you weren't going to be haymaking, he was looking over the gate at the bottom. It seemed as if they knew. You used to take oats to catch them with. You had to get a head collar over it.

Well, they got to know. You would keep it lower down, so that when they bent their heads down you could pop it over their heads. But they could put their heads out and get a bite before you could – so you'd to be quite sharp to get them caught. Especially as time went on, because they'd get sick of haytiming, what for clegs and midges, and one thing and another. Because they had

a hard time, had horses. Like first thing on the morning, you used to start 'bout 5 o'clock, as you had to have the grass cut while the dew was still on. So, then they got a little bit of rest. And then once the sun got up and then they had to be turning and strewing. They were full days, they were.

Des Collinson

Why, you got taken to your horses, I mean, they were like one of the family. I know when they went, when we did away with the horses, it was a sad day to see the horses going, it were.

Jack Addison

'Dolly' with hay rake at West Briscoe Farm, Baldersdale, early 1950s. Farmer Wilf Allinson (in cap) stands with some relatives from Durham who had come to help out at hay time.

William Bell (Wilf Allinson's brother-in-law) leading hay to the shed.

'Hay time - it blighted my life.'
4 days? 4 months? Or even longer...

Once the sward had been cut, the haymaking itself could begin – strewing, turning, gathering the hay up into small heaps (their sizes varied greatly from 'foot-cocks' or 'half rucks' to 'coconut macaroon'-shaped stacks called 'pikes') and rowing up.

Now we had another old friend, an old relation, and he used to reckon four good days would make hay. He'd cut it one day, either turn it the second or the third, and he would have it into... it was pikes of hay then, or baling before the finish, and he'd have it gathered up on the fourth.

John Dodd

It went on for weeks and you ended up with stuff that was hardly worth picking up. But if you were fortunate and got a summer like we've just seen lately we would have managed wonderful. Oh, we'd be finished in a week.

Alan Scott

But in the old days there were many years when we finished in September or October; blighted my life, hay time. Before this bag silage came in and the round bales we never had a summer, it was always spent haytiming because we get so little weather, normally, to get it.

Eileen Bentley

Helping hands
Neighbour helped neighbour in those days:

In Edmundbyers help from different sources was sometimes possible. Here farmer Ted Kirton (with trilby hat) poses with the youth hostel warden and a group of her hostellers who were roped in to help at hay time! The photo was taken by another helper, Heiner Ruhe, a German prisoner of war assigned to work on Ted's Village Farm.

Well, I'll tell you what it was in those days, say, we got finished ourselves. Well, you see, you got your cows milked on a night, and it was a lovely fine night, and you would see a neighbour busy or you'll say, "Well, I'll just give him a hand." And you went and you got your suppers and you thought you'd had a good night out, you know, people did in those days. But nowadays, like, people won't, you know, it's all changed, that, now, people don't do anything, they want paying. But that was how it was in those days, for neighbours helped each other, aye.

Jack Addison

Neighbours pitch in.

A neighbour forking loose hay into the bowel hole in the hay loft on Brockersgill Farm. Note the shadowy figure inside. This work of spreading and trampling down the hay on top of the 'mow' was, according to Hannah Hauxwell, the hottest and dustiest work of all at hay time – and often given to young girls on the farm to do!

A woman's work

And while haytiming was going on there were all the other jobs around the farm to be done – much of it by the women.

The women did everything on a Dales farm, both summer and winter. Mother fed the calves and milked and went out in wintertime. The woman went out both summer and winter, she was both woman and man really.

It wasn't easy because the ladies, in the dales further down country mebbe not, or if they had sufficient hired help – but often when they were just family farms, the wife helped with the haytiming. And then, you know, cooked and baked, so it was hard on women folks. 'Cos people had to eat, and meals to prepare, and baking. And jam, see the nuisance would be the berries would be ready, if you had a garden and berries, in hay time and so you mebbe picked a bit either before you went out or, if it was a dull day, you went to pick berries. It was marvellous, mother used to make a nice blackcurrant pie and made some botanic beer, that was in a nice stone jar. It wasn't alcoholic!

Hannah Hauxwell

There was quite a lot of baking because there was a lot of people to feed in those days. Well, you saw that photograph,* there must have been an awful lot of sandwiches or something prepared for that! Washing day Monday; Tuesday I think was bedrooms; Wednesday you went to market – you went to Barney anyway... to sell any surplus eggs or butter. Thursday was baking day, Friday was buttermaking day.

Peggy Nixon

Carrie Raine – with young Eric Wilkinson hitching a ride! – sweeping hay at Mickleton in the 1930s. Standing on the back rail of the sweep helped weigh it down, and was fairly safe. Note Carrie is wearing white gloves which helped prevent blisters and sore hands when using ropes and wooden rake handles for hours on end.

* See p. 25

Healthy work?

There is a danger, though, looking back at what we would call today the 'community spirit' that undoubtedly existed, that we may be drawn into thinking that it was a better time altogether for man and beast. In the words of the song, that 'ain't necessarily so'; rose-tinted vision and hindsight are not the same thing.

There was a disease called 'Farmer's Lung', the dust and spores out of bad hay, working among it and breathing it in winter. It was a dreadful problem; it was a form of emphysema.

David Bentley

As Neville Turner, respected Teesdale vet for 30 years who retired in 2000, says:

Whilst well-made hay is today still the prime objective of the farmer, he now has a second option. The technique of wrapping big bales of wilted grass in plastic ensures anaerobic conditions where the product is guaranteed to become high quality silage or 'haylage'.

Early silage making in the 1950s, East Briscoe Farm, Baldersdale.

For the first time in history, good winter rations do not depend on a good summer. Previously, in a bad summer, hay crops would lie in the in the field, wet and rotting until some improvement in the weather when haymaking could resume. The resultant leached hay lost much of its nutritive value.

In addition the dampness provided ideal conditions for fungal growth, and the hay would be full of fungal spores which erupted in clouds when it was cut and fed to the stock in winter. A winter eating hay with little or no nutritive value caused dramatic loss in condition of the stock. Some became emaciated and in extreme cases 'went off their legs'. In addition, the fungal spores caused illness in both the stock and the farmers, the commonest of which was aspergillosis or 'farmer's lung'.

Neville Turner

The End

When hay time ended depended entirely on the weather – and it was certainly not a time to celebrate. Everyone was too exhausted with the effort of winning the hay and, if you'd got yours in, your neighbour may still have needed help with his:

There was very few farmers finished haytiming after I left school, before 12th August. And we still used to go (grouse) beating even though we weren't finished here. Of course we were back home five o'clock, round about, and... it was only about that time of the day that normally we started to sweep hay in. There was no five o'clock on our calendars.

Bill Nixon

I think you were pleased to be done and that was it, like, and you were worn out in the field. It was hard work, like, aye, it was hard work.

Jack Addison

I don't remember any celebrations. We'd just mebbe say, "Thank God that's over!"

Bill Nixon

You sat down a bit and says, "That's it!"

Connie Wearmouth

Manuring

Farmyard manure – 'muck from the midden heaps' – was the only fertiliser used to replace the nutrients lost by taking an annual hay crop from the meadows.

During the winter in suitable weather, when it was either fairly dry or possibly a little bit frozen, you could cart your muck out without doing any damage. Of course years ago when I started you led the muck out in little carts and put it out in heaps and spread it by hand.

David Bentley

Wheysike, Upper Teesdale 1934.

So, with horse and cart you would, with what we called a 'gripe', fork the manure into the cart, and then lead it to the field. Then we had what we called a muck drag with a handle, we called it a shaft, and we had one with three claws... you pulled it out. You needed a decent quiet horse, not one that was inclined to bolt. Every so often you pulled it into a heap, mebbe the height of the table. So you led your manure into heaps, then somebody had to go and spread it with the fork.

Hannah Hauxwell

Now at that time, rather oddly enough, all carts were on iron wheels and you couldn't very well take an iron-wheeled cart onto land when it was wet. So your middens used to get rather big and come a dry spell or a frosty spell, you had to take advantage.

Bill Nixon

Muck spreading by hand.

Harrowing

Often while the lambs were still in the fields and with birds nesting, the meadows would be harrowed to spread out the muck and level any molehills.

You had to harrow, yes, aye... when the weather was right, in March usually, while the lambs were still there. You just carried on, like, aye, to level them out. Where you manured it, it was rough, it'd be harrowed in a bit, like. You sort of knew the nests were there 'cause, when you got near, they used to come diving down. You used to try to avoid them, you know, yes... aye.

Jack Addison

Why, there was one field, there was sometimes a dozen or thirteen nests in, ya know. But we never harrowed them out, like, because there's one thing, like, there's two birds that're really farmer's friends because they go for wireworms does lapwings. Lapwings is one. They'll not come an' pinch ya hen feed where your hen house is at; they'll not come an' pinch your corn an' all, will not lapwings. Crows will like, and some of them, but lapwings never did and they'll not come in your garden and eat your berries or anything like that. An t'other's swallows. They'll never harm a farmer like, swallows and lapwings is two nicest birds there is.

Derek Wearmouth

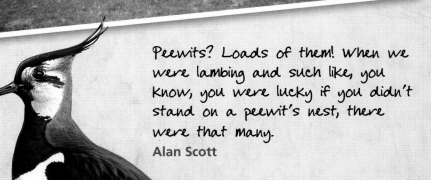

Bernard Hooper harrowing with 'Dapper' in Big Field, Brockersgill Farm, Newbiggin-in-Teesdale in the 1950s.

Peewits? Loads of them! When we were lambing and such like, you know, you were lucky if you didn't stand on a peewit's nest, there were that many.

Alan Scott

Farmer's friend – the lapwing, or 'peewit'

Mowing

One man went to mow… but, if he was lucky, he might have had a team of helpers or at least a fellow hand to follow behind with a rake.

The single-horse grass cutters, they were murder. They took that much pulling really, to drive the knife and that, it took a lot of horse power.

Bill Nixon

The single-horse grass cutters have a 3 foot 6 cutter bar and a double-horse, where you put two horses in, they were 4 foot 6. At one time we got a Pierce grass cutter. They'd been made in Ireland, these — there wasn't many of them about — and they were 4 foot. They were all to sharpen before you could start off and you really had to have them sharpened — stones and anything like that was spoiling them.

Des Collinson

They just cut in little 'setts', about what they could manage — they put into hay pikes in them days — about what they could manage to pike in an afternoon… and there would be a sett cut, and a sett lying drying, another sett turned, and then the sett which they were piking.

John Dodd

A single-horse mower cutting a field of grass, while two men rake out the clumps afterwards, at Huntshieldford near St John's Chapel in Weardale. Two more men with scythes are either opening out access to the field or cutting a part too difficult for the mower.

Horse-drawn single-bar cutter 'in the hayfield' in Allendale.

Scything

The days when gangs of men – some of them Irish who might come back to the same farm each year – worked in teams to mow a meadow with scythes all but disappeared soon after the Second World War. By the 1950s and 60s scythes were only really used to cut the grass where machines could not reach.

In the old time, there used to be gangs go around contracting with a scythe. They reckoned a good man would mow an acre a day. Gangs of six and eight would go round and that way they'd mow from six to eight acres.

John Dodd

I always remember these three men – we're going back 70 years – they had a scythe each and there was straight shank then, a great long shank, and there was three men and one of them had a beard and they were doing this hillside and they were just walking away you know... Nobody could do it now, nobody would know how to do... it was grand... you know, I often think about that, like, aye...

Jack Addison

They used to hack the wall backs, after they'd mown it they'd go round and what you called 'hack the dyke back'. In those days, it would barely be a foot; they could get a lot closer to the walls than we can nowadays. And the last memory of that, I can remember somebody, a chap called Lenny Gill, down Langleydale, he was the last person I saw hacking a field and that was in '86.

Elizabeth Hooper

Two different scythes – one straight, one curved.

The Lowe family from Bank Cottage, Middleton-in-Teesdale scything at hay time.

John Willy Pratt sharpening and mowing grass with a scythe on Hilltop Farm, St John's Chapel, Weardale, c.1910.

Turning and Strewing

After mowing, depending on the weather and what the farmer had available, a combination of horse-drawn machines and hand tools – turners and strewers and hand rakes – might be used to turn the hay and spread it about so it could dry.

Generally it would start pretty early in the morning, be finished by ten o'clock so they could get on turning or raking up ready for piking or something like that. But if it came a wet day they may get on and cut a whole field down. But anyway, the next thing was turning it... we had a Blackstone turner. I have known, mind, when there was plenty of labour, I have known them turn it with the hand rakes, if it had lain, y'know, if it had come 'stoppy' weather and it had gotten grown in a bit, they thought they could pull it out better with the hand rakes.

John Dodd

And then we had what we called a strewer, it used to strew it, it was good thing. It was another implement, you had the turner and then we had this one that used to dash it about, what we called a strewer.

Jack Addison

Well, it... was a machine with two rows of teeth on, that used to spin round, and throw it about, and obviously we hoped it brought the green to the top and dry to the bottom, and it was sometimes to do two or three times, obviously depending upon the weather. We had, if we had time, or it was necessary, we used to hand turn it, and that was a slow job. Well, hand

Rear view of a strewer.

turning, you could be more precise of getting the green to the top, and the dry to the bottom. Sometimes when you were on with the strewer, and if there was a big heap for some reason or other, why it strewed it, but it didn't strew it out like that. It just went over the top and dropped the same amount as what it took up... When you did it by hand, you could spread them lumps about because, where there was a lump, there was mebbe a bit of spare land with nowt on, and you would even it out and you could make a far better job of it by hand stirring it than you could by machine. But it was too laborious.

Selwyn Watson

John Dawson with horse-drawn strewer at Peghorn, Harwood-in-Teesdale, late 1940s.

Raking

Every last bit of hay would be raked up by hand; hardly a stalk was wasted. But you could tell a 'townie' from a local…

And you cut it and then it was turned, now that's another thing. If the weather was bad and it rained and rained and rained, the implements weren't that good in those days and some of the implements didn't make a very good job of turning it over, you had to go out with hand rakes, turning it over with hand rakes, if the weather was that bad, but really you just turned it. The weather had a lot to do with it, same as it had now, like…

Jack Addison

If you had people not used to the work, say who lived in towns — a lot of people had relations who'd gone to work in coalmines when the leadmines were finished and that — they used to come, but if you saw them, you know, you could pick them out, as they usually travelled raking backwards.

Des Collinson

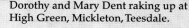
Dorothy and Mary Dent raking up at High Green, Mickleton, Teesdale.

Three ladies with rakes at Forcegarth Farm, in Upper Teesdale c1920. The farm was worked by a tenant farmer Mr Tomas Gibson (known as 'Grandee'). The woman on the left is Miss Jennie Gibson from Widdybank Farm (sister to Grandee); on the right is Mrs Nancy Ireland (nee Beadle) a visitor; and in the middle, Miss Nanny Beadle, a servant at Forcegarth - she was engaged to the farm's hired hand, Tom O'Tyne. Unfortunately, shortly after this photo was taken, Tom's horse reared up at Steps Corner, just above High Force Quarry, and he was killed.

Hand raking at Grassholme farm in Lunedale, 1940s.

Rowing Up

Horse rakes were used to gather the hay up into rows ready for the next stage – making it into pikes or sweeping it to the barns or stacks.

Then, if you were lucky, it would be hay and then you'd draw it up with a horse and a horse rake and then you had this put into row only you had to put them into little heaps somehow so what you'd call the sweep would come along with usually two horses and a sweep and sweep it to where you wanted it, and it was all to do with... it was all hand, like, aye, it was all hand...

Jack Addison

John Wearmouth, aged 12, on a horse rake at Brumwell Street, Ettersgill in Upper Teesdale.

Sweeping

In the old horse days you used to have a 'wing sweep', like a gate on the back with a horse on each corner, and these things, sometimes they picked it up and sometimes they didn't. But what it did used to do was roll the hay underneath and you got these, like, rolls of hay that could be anything from an inch and a half to four inches thick and you had to pull these bloody things to bits. Oh, I used to hate it, absolutely hated pulling these rolls of hay to bits which you just rolled up, aye, just little rolls.

Willy Wearmouth

A 'paddy sweep', near Bowes.

The wing sweep was the more usual type used for hay in the North Pennine dales. Here a load of hay has just been dropped at a new stack in a meadow near Bowes in the 1920s. The hauling chain is being reconnected to one of the wings of the sweep.

Haymaking at Saddlebow in Lunedale using a wing sweep. The pair of horses, belonging to Joe Longstaff of neighbouring Greengates, were twins.

Hay cocks and half rucks, kyles and pikes

Once dry, the hay could be gathered up into small heaps of various sizes – and nomenclature! If it rained they would have to be strewed out again to dry. The largest of these were the pikes. Once made into pikes, with the tops fastened with hay rope, the hay could stay for days or even weeks while haymaking could carry on elsewhere on the farm.

When it was the pikes, if it was dry it made beautiful hay, lovely scented hay, really beautiful hay, better than they get today I should imagine.
Fred Stocks

My Dad was rather particular about making pikes. There would be about two sweep load go into one pike. But when he got them up they were well rounded out at top and he used to rake them down and they were really nice and neat. And then they would stand there for a while and... often at that time there wasn't many pike bogeys. He just used to put a chain round bottom of the pike and fasten it to the horse just pull them up to the shed or whatever you wanted and stack. No balers those days!
Bill Nixon

We just used to make hay ropes. After you'd got your pikes built, and you just had someone at the bottom of the pike, just feeding bits of grass hay

Note the neat rows of pikes and half rucks in the field across the road from the Hooper family and their horse-drawn hay sweep.

out, and you put it round a couple of teeth on your rake, you kept spinning your rake, and just feeding it out and spinning, until you'd got a long length and make a rope. You'd use your rake at one end and you could use it to put it over the top and then you'd tuck them in. And it's surprising how they kept the tops from blowing off.
Des Collinson

Irishmen used to come over from County Mayo and offer their services for a month at hay time. I had a very good man who helped me for a year or two. He was called Paddy... Patrick Kieran. He taught me how to build these pikes. The hay's either swept or in some way it's delivered into a central point in the field, and you just build it like a little haystack, just the same as building a little haystack, and a good pike would hold anywhere from half a ton upwards.
David Bentley

Mr Bentley with pikes at Kelton, in Lunedale.

Hay time tea

Hay time teas were a time to rest for both humans and horses, and a photographer often seemed to be on hand!

The basket that the baby's in was called a 'corn skep'. Now the story behind that was that my father used to have... I think he had two ploughing fields that he sowed. One we called Little Green Gate field, and the one over the railway was Top Ploughing Field. And he obviously sowed the corn by hand and this you strapped round... It was a corn skep and it's shaped at this side to fit and it had a strap. But that was a brand new one and I think when he'd bought it they hadn't got anywhere to put the baby, so that was used for several generations actually, for a new baby.

Peggy Nixon

Hay time tea with pikes. Note the hay rope used to tie down the top of the pike on the left.

A hay time tea mug from Catton, Allendale.

The year is 1915 and the Birkett family, friends and farmworkers gather for a hay time tea with the photographer at West Park, Cotherstone – a dozen all told. (A dozen? Count them! And don't forget the baby John in the basket!)

Leading the hay

There were several different ways of getting the hay from the meadows to where it was to be stored for the winter – by snigging, sledging and sweeping or with a pike bogey or hay cart. The method depended on how far the meadows were from the farmyards, or where the stack was to be made, and the nature of the land they had to cross in order to get there.

Snigging

There was a way of what we used to call 'snigging' them which was to put a chain around them and drag them to the barn. Once the pikes had settled and solidified they would stand pulling quite a long way. And it did save a lot of work if you could get right to the barn with them.

David Bentley

Snigging was the simplest way of moving a pike. A chain was put round the pike which had settled nicely so the whole thing could just be dragged to the barn or stack.

Sledging

'Sledding hay', Brumwell Street, Teesdale in the early 1950s.

Horse-drawn sledge leading hay, St John's Chapel, c.1910.

'Mr. Pattison's Pictures'

The Rev. James Pattison became vicar of St John's Chapel in Weardale in 1906 when he was 53. He was to live and work there until his death in 1936. He was a very keen photographer and hay time was one of his most popular subjects. As a result, we are fortunate to have today some classic images of the various stages of hay time in Weardale from a century or so ago, such as the one shown above. Several of his photographs have been selected for this book – to identify them, see the photo credits on page 38. Many more can be found in the photographic archives at Beamish Museum – see page 37 for more information.

Pike bogey

Winching a pike onto the splendidly named 'pike bogey' could be a tricky operation. A chain was passed round the pike and the handle turned to ratchet the pike onto the platform. Once the pike had passed the tipping point of the two-wheeled cart, the platform would tip forward and the horse could set off across the fields to the barn or stack.

We used to go for the pikes with the hay bogey — that was my sister and me. We would tip it up. Sometimes it took both of us to tip it up. And then you'd put a rope round, and it had a handle with a big cog and a pole on it. Oh, I can remember that now, with the long handle, both of us trying to click, click, click as this pole dropped in. And then sometimes if your rope would be digging in and come too far, and sometimes you could come right through underneath, and your pike would still be sitting. But once you got on, you know, you didn't do that too oft. And then you had to pull them far enough up the bogey past the centre of gravity, and then the handle came down and you put a pin in and then you would lead them to where you were going and tip them off. Usually to tip them off, you would take the rope off, tip them up, and somebody would stand at the other side with a fork, get stuck in, and then the horse would come out and they would just drop off.

Des Collinson

Farmer Isaac Davidson winds a pike of hay onto a pike bogey at Loaning Head Farm, Garrigill near Alston, c.1950. His daughter Anne looks on with a broken wrist in plaster. Tom, the horse, stands slightly downhill to ease the weight while one young lad tries to get a lift up as the hay slides onto the bogey's platform. The pike has been covered - or 'bagged' - with an opened-up hessian meal bag held on with ropes at each corner or even with twisted hay ropes passed over the top.

Winching a pike onto the hay bogey.

Hay cart

More unusually in the North Pennine dales a hay cart or wagon would be used.

A group leading a hay wagon pulled by a team of three horses near Middleton-in-Teesdale.

Storing the hay

Finally the hay would be stored – forked into barns or field houses or made into stacks.

They'd be just to fork in, through what we call 'hay bowels' – some were very high. The back's not so bad but round the front and on a hot day they were really killing. Whitewashed walls and forking that, and you had to have a long fork and then you had to have maybe a couple of people inside – one would be taking the hay back and the other one would be levelling it out and walking around trampling it down – because that was the thing, you had to keep tightening, levelling and trampling down. If you just put it inside you were soon stuck, you know, you had to keep getting it away, so you could get t'other in.

Des Collinson

Often if there was women about in the family, they got the job in the mow... as you forked it up they took it from what they call the bowel hole. And she would fork it back to somebody else, and do you know, working among that loose hay I have often thought that was the hardest job of haytiming. It was the hottest and dustiest.

Bill and Peggy Nixon

Rather than a long lead you would stack them in the field. You would put bushes down for the bottom. Well, branches, so the bottom didn't go rotten, then you would stack her up. We topped it out, we used to do it with straw, put straw and a net and then they used to pull the sides to get the shape, you could get a right good shape, aye. Instead of long straggles comin' out, I used to pull the sides.

Willy Wearmouth

Horse pulling a pike and bogey at Carrshield, Allendale, 1934.

At least 15 workers and two horses pose on and in front of a hay stack near Rookhope, Weardale in 1912.

Donkey on a stack, Edmundbyers – proof that four-legged animals were also used occasionally to help tread down the hay! A young Ernie Walton leans against a pike in the foreground.

Feeding the stock

With the barns full, farmers could breathe a sigh of relief in the knowledge that – hopefully, if it didn't spoil – they had plenty of feed for their animals over winter.

A sharp, heavy and cumbersome hay spade was used to cut a 'dess' of hay – as much as you could lift or carry with the spike, seen here held in the right hand.

It was stacked in the barns in hay mows which used to settle and heat up if you hadn't got it very dry, you had to watch the heating situation, it would spoil the hay, of course, if it was in any way damp.

David Bentley

It would come out beautiful stuff, oh aye. You would feed it up and next day it was down here, it had settled you know, especially if it had heated. Then you would cut it out with a hay spade. It was just solid, it would come out rather like 'baccy' – tobacco – just light brown, depending how hot it got, like, aye. (Was there danger it would catch fire?) Yes, aye, oh aye, there was. Sometimes you used to have a sack in the middle full of straw, hay and as you built it up you pulled this up and it left a chimney, otherwise that bit there with hay spade diggin' a hole you were about gassed.

Willy Wearmouth

That stack was just the colour of ginger cake. It had turned really brown, but anyway it was more like silage than hay! But the animals loved it.

Fred Stocks

In winter in the stacks, even in the barns, you had hay spades to cut the hay, because sometimes you wanted your best hay for the sheep, so you would take what we call a 'dess'. You needed good sharp spades as well, had to keep them sharp... You would cut a bit, roughly mebbe twice the size of the table or, if you were going to tie it up to carry on your back, well you wouldn't want it as big as that, 'cos you used to take the hay up for the sheep, or if the horses were with them, in the allotments.

Hannah Hauxwell

Bernard Hooper leading hay on a sledge from the barn to fields to feed sheep in winter, Brockersgill Farm, Newbiggin-in-Teesdale in 1950s.

Winter foddering at Spital Valley Farm, Bowes in the 1960s – transition time from horse and sledge to tractor and back box.

Transition time

The late 1950s – early 1960s was 'transition time' for many of the hill farms in the North Pennines, perhaps no better illustrated than by these three photos spanning a decade at one farm, Forcegarth, in Upper Teesdale. In the mid 50s everything was still done with horses and hand tools. The first tractors arrived, and with them balers, by the end of that decade.

Along with mechanisation came agricultural intensification – seen here is the very first 'seed hay' produced in Teesdale. 'Seed hay' (as opposed to 'old land hay') is produced by ploughing up and reseeding the meadow very 2-3 years with only productive species, such as rye grass.

Forcegarth 1955 – Hay time with horses.

Three generations of the Beadle family. Roy sits on the hay rake with his father Philip behind and his daughter Rita standing between the two boys.

Forcegarth 1959 – Hay time with a David Brown tractor and New Holland baler.

Roy Beadle rakes up on the right while his cousin Frank Walton drives the tractor. Frank was the first person in Teesdale to own a baler and go contracting.

Forcegarth 1966 – A huge crop of 'seed hay' but where have all the flowers gone?

Roy Beadle on a 'little grey Fergie'. It wasn't all smooth running: the single-bar cutter kept breaking down due to the rough ground and heavy crop.

Gone but not forgotten

With mechanisation and intensification came not only a loss of wildflowers but other wildlife too – including the iconic corncrake.

Yes, we had the corncrakes, oh, quite a few of those. I remember those vividly. Specially in t'little three acre we called West Field. But you see, people started haytiming earlier, silaging unfortunately did away with the corncrake.

Bill Nixon

Well, when we were young like, there was corncrakes. And then they stopped coming like. I'm not sure really (when they stopped) but what happened was, you see, they weren't just up Teesdale they were farther down and they started taking two crops off for silage. As soon as they started silaging in a big way they took an early crop off, an' I think they just, you know, chopped nests to bits, like, when they were nesting. They just stopped coming like. They never came back. It was between ploughing and... two crops of silage. As soon as they did that it was the end of the corncrake, ya know.

Willy Wearmouth

The corncrake

Is it too much to hope that one day, through sensitive farm management, the evocative rasping call of the corncrake may once again be heard in the North Pennines?

Meadow Memories: Pen Portraits

Jack Addison

Born at Briscoe Farm in Baldersdale 'one dipping day' in 1925. Left school at 14 and farmed until he retired in 1998. Seen here on 'the stack that Jack built', his first, in the late 1940s.

David & Eileen Bentley

Moved to Lanehead at Kelton in Lunedale in 1962 from Malham in the Yorkshire Dales where an Irishman, hired for a month at hay time, taught David to build pikes.

Des Collinson

Moved to Woodside Farm in Newbiggin in Teesdale in 1937 when he was 3 and has farmed there all his life. The farm has been in the family since the 1820s.

John Dodd

Has lived all his life on Sillywrea Farm near Langley in Allendale. He sprang to fame in 2001 as 'The Last Horseman' with a book and TV film made about 'Britain's only horse-powered farm'.

Hannah Hauxwell

Became an unlikely, and reluctant, national celebrity following a 1970s Yorkshire TV programme 'Too Long a Winter' that featured her hard, solitary life farming at Low Birk Hatt in Baldersdale.

Robert & Elizabeth Hooper

Robert, son of Bernard and Elizabeth, was born in 1964 and recalls hay time as a child at Brockersgill Farm in Newbiggin in Teesdale taking up most of the summer holidays!

Bill & Peggy Nixon

Peggy, Cotherstone Carnival Queen in 2005 aged 85, was born Margaret Birkett at West Park Farm in Baldersdale while her husband Bill, who began working as an agricultural contractor in the 1950s, cut and baled many a meadow in Teesdale.

Alan Scott

Born and raised in Upper Teesdale. When his father died he took over the running of Widdybank Farm, part of the National Nature Reserve, and went on to become a Durham County Councillor and founding trustee of UTASS.

Fred Stocks

Born in 1920, after an eventful life that included surviving the Malta Convoy while with the RAF in the Second World War, 'Muggins' settled down with his wife Flora to a relatively peaceful farming life at High Light Shield at Mohope in Allendale.

Selwyn Watson

Farmed at Rivelin, high above Newbiggin in Upper Teesdale, and saw many changes brought about by mechanisation and conversion from dairy to suckler herds. Seen here at the High Force Hotel in 1980 with the Barclays Bank Trophy for best hay!

Derek & Connie Wearmouth

Like many in Upper Teesdale, their father was both quarryman and farmer. With just 26 acres and a small dairy herd to begin with, Derek took on the tenancy of English Hill farm from the Raby Estate until retiring in 2003.

Willy Wearmouth

Born in 1927 on a Raby Estate farm, he farmed at Middle End near Middleton from 1962 until '74 when he left to join the prison service.

John Rudd & Son
Britain's last commercial wooden hay rake makers

Graeme (left) and John Rudd assembling the rakes. No glue is used to hold the different parts together.

> The basic design hasn't altered in my time and I think my grandfather adopted it so it could have had 100 years at least, maybe longer. The rakes are all put together tight, the teeth are put in by pressure. And there's four nails hold the rake together when it's finished. Three go along the head, two through the bow, one through the shaft, then one goes through the shaft into the bow lower down.
>
> **John Rudd**

Entering John Rudd's workshop in Dufton, below the Pennine escarpment in Cumbria, is like stepping back into another age. Accompanied by his son Graeme who works alongside him, the various parts of the hay rake – head, bow and shaft – are assembled in a room with a large open fireplace, dating from the 1630s, in much the same way as they must have been for well over a century. Surrounded by old tools, bits of discarded wood and sawdust, father and son still make 10,000 hay rakes a year. Sadly, though, few of them are used for their original purpose these days – they find greater demand from gardeners, golf clubs and athletics stadia, for raking leaves and smoothing the sand in bunkers and long jump pits.

The business was started by John's grandfather in the 1890s, and after the Second World War his father started modernising the production process by introducing various electrically-driven machines that could speed up most of the repetitive jobs like planing the shaft, boring the holes in the head and sharpening the teeth. Not all the new machines required power though – a wooden 'shaper', an ingenious device made by a German prisoner of war who worked with John's father, is still used today for bending the bows to the required shape.

John Rudd stands, left, with his father, John Joseph Rudd, outside their workshop in the 1980s with a selection of three different types of rake.

These days all timber is sourced from sustainable forests. The shaft, head and bow are all made from ash, the teeth from silver birch.

'Hay Time Talk' – a glossary of hay time terms

aftermath   what is left to graze in the meadow after the hay has been removed. Trampling by livestock is important because it creates small bare areas where seeds can grow

bogey/ pike bogey   a type of horse-drawn cart, basically a platform mounted on two wheels, which could tip up so that pikes could be winched onto it and then removed, or led, from the field

bowel hole/ forking hole   the small door roughly half way up the wall of the barn where the hay would be forked in, before being levelled out and trampled down

cock/foot-cock/ wap/wapping   a small, roughly conical, heap of hay (about knee height) made by hand-raking. When everything used to be done by hand, this would be part of the normal method of making hay; with the advent of horse-drawn machinery, they were usually only made if the weather was particularly poor and/or to break up the rows of hay if a sweep were being used

dash/dashing   spread/spreading the hay about with rakes after the swathes have been turned

dess   a portion of hay, about 2'6" (1m) square, cut with a spade from the mow (qv) to feed livestock

field house   a characteristic building in the upper dales: a combination of byre and barn, to house cattle and hay where you could 'lead manure out and get hay in'

fog   used by farmers rather than 'aftermath' (qv) – the grasses that grow in the meadows after the hay has been cut and led from the meadows, often used to fatten livestock before they are taken to market

hack/hacking   as in 'hack the wall backs', to cut down the grass close to the walls (where the machines could not reach) with a scythe

hayrake   a two wheeled horse-drawn machine with many prongs designed to gather hay into windrows

hay rope   used to tie down the tops of pikes, made by twisting and teasing out lengths of hay either with the teeth of a hay rake or using a thrawcrook (qv)

kyle   'an outsized coconut maroon'-shaped heap of hay, smaller than a pike (qv)

lead   to take the hay from a field, e.g. by sledge or pike bogey

mow   v. to cut the grass in a meadow, which would always begin early in the morning; n. (rhymes with 'cow') the term given to the hay once it has been stored in the barn

pike   a large hay cock, carefully built to turn water with combed down sides, and typically up to about 10-12 feet (4m) high with a circular 6 foot (2m) base. Might be built if weather was poor, or there was no room to store in a barn, and would keep until ready for use, or time was available to lead into the barn, using a pike bogey or sledge

platts/plot   see setts

puttens   small heaps of hay (cf 'waps') made by breaking up the rows, thus making it easier to sweep when using a horse-drawn rake

rick/half-rick   (also ruck/half-ruck) a small stack of hay

setts/settings/ platts	the amount of hay that could be cut and piked in a day, so that it would not be spoilt, so 'a sett cut, a sett lying drying, another turned, and the sett they were piking'
sledge/sled	wooden platform on runners pulled by a horse between the windrows, used to load hay and lead it from the meadows where they were relatively flat, if the hay didn't need to be led too far or along tracks to be stored
snigging	pulling or dragging a pike with a chain, possible where the ground was reasonably flat and the barn close by, thus avoiding the need to load onto a sledge or pike bogey
strew	(rhymes with 'now') to spread and turn the hay once it has been cut so that it might dry more quickly. Formerly done by hand with both men and women typically working across a meadow using rakes, later replaced by horse-drawn machinery
strickle	a small wooden tool for sharpening a scythe, usually kept handily attached near the top of the scythe pole/shaft. Its pitted wooden surface would be sprinkled with mutton fat (kept in a horn) and soft sand (kept in a drawstring bag) to make an effective and abrasive whetstone
sward	the vegetation found in the meadow
swathe	the heaps of grass, etc, left lying in the meadow after it has been mown
swathe-turner	horse-drawn machine used to turn swathes, could also be used to make windrows
sweep	horse-drawn contraption dragged along the ground to gather in the hay from windrows into larger cocks or pikes. Different types were in use in the dales, e.g. 'gate', 'wing'/'winged' or 'paddy' sweeps

ted/tedding	turning the hay. Also 'tedder', a machine for so doing
thrawcrook	a small hand tool used for twisting hay to make hay rope (illustrated below)
windrow	(also 'winrows') rows of hay
wuffler	(pronounced 'woofler') a tractor-driven machine used for strewing the hay

Please note: Many of the terms used to describe haymaking processes, tools and horse-drawn machinery are shown photographically in Marie Hartley and Joan Ingilby's book (see p.37).

Top tips on seeing meadows at their best

The best time to see our meadows in most years is from early June to mid July. To the layperson, for ten months of the year a meadow will look much like any other field. It is only when the farmer has removed his stock around the end of April and 'shut up' the meadows that they start to burst into life. Many of our "best meadows" are on farms in a 'Higher Level Stewardship' agreement which requires the farmer not to cut before July 15th in order to give more of the characteristic hay meadow plants a chance to set their seed. So, if you leave it much later than that hay time will be in full swing – especially if the sun is shining!

Hay Time walks

The North Pennines AONB Partnership has produced a series of three walk leaflets around some colourful meadows in the North Pennines – in Allendale, Weardale and Baldersdale. Download them from the AONB's website or contact the Partnership's offices in Stanhope (see address below).

Hannah's Meadow

At Low Birk Hatt, in Baldersdale just off the Pennine Way north of Blackton reservoir, one of Hannah Hauxwell's old meadows is now owned and managed as a nature reserve by the Durham Wildlife Trust. A restored field house containing a small exhibition offers shelter and an insight into the wildlife you can see in the meadow.

Events

Each year one or more of these organisations may hold a guided walk to see the hay meadows in the North Pennines as part of their programme of events. Check out their websites:

Durham County Council - www.durham.gov.uk/countryside

Durham Wildlife Trust (for Hannah's Meadow) - www.durhamwt.myzen.co.uk

Forestry Commission (for Hamsterley Forest) - www.forestry.gov.uk

Natural England (for Moor House - Upper Teesdale National Nature Reserve) - www.naturalengland.org.uk

North Pennines AONB Partnership - www.northpennines.org.uk

Further information from:

North Pennines AONB Partnership
Weardale Business Centre, The Old Co-op Building,
1 Martin Street, Stanhope, County Durham DL13 2UY

t: 01388 528801
e: info@northpenninesaonb.org.uk
www.northpennines.org.uk
facebook.com/NorthPenninesAONB
twitter.com/NorthPennAONB

The AONB Partnership has a Green Tourism award for its corporate office.

GOLD

Where to find out more

Beamish Museum

At Home Farm a fine collection of old hay time machinery and hand tools is housed. In the Learning Resource Centre, the oral history archives (including the AONB Partnership's Hay Time interviews from which the quotes in this book were taken), extensive historic photographic collections and old agricultural catalogues, etc, can be accessed or see: www.beamish.org.uk

Weardale Museum, Ireshopeburn

An interesting collection of local hay time artefacts, plus computerised records from the 'War Ag.' farm survey for Weardale. www.weardalemuseum.co.uk

Publications

The following books have more information about hay time in the North Pennines and related subjects:

Bowden, C. 'The Last Horsemen: A year at Sillywrea, Britain's only horse-powered farm', Granada, 2001.

Bradshaw, M.E. & Turner, J. 'Origin and History of the Teesdale Flora' in 'The Natural History of Upper Teesdale', DWT 4th ed. 2003.

Evans, G. E. 'Ask the Fellows who Cut the Hay', London: Faber and Faber, 1965.

Gamble, D. & St. Pierre, T. (eds.) 'Hay Time in the Yorkshire Dales – the natural, cultural and land management history of hay meadows', Scotforth Books, 2010.

Hartley, M. & Ingilby, J. 'Hay-time', chapter in 'Life and Traditions in the Yorkshire Dales', Dalesman Books, 1989 (first published by Dent & Sons in 1968).

Hauxwell, H. with Cockcroft, B. 'Hannah: The Complete Story', Arrow Books London 1992.

Lunedale Heritage Project, 'More of Lunedale's Heritage', Mosaic (Teesdale), 2010.

Turner, N. 'Hill Farmer: A working year on the fells', Dalesman, 2001.

www.hayinart.com
An amazing online collection of over 6500 great 'works of hay' in both art and literature.

Acknowledgements

The editors would like to thank all those who have helped in the making of this book, and especially those interviewed who shared their hay time memories and gave us permission to freely use their photographs.

Photo credits

Jack Addison (p.15); Fred Allinson (p.12 right); Maude and Rita, the wife and daughter of the late Roy Beadle (p.30); Beamish Museum (p.12 left, 18, 19 lower left, 21 left, 27 bottom, 28 left & centre, 29 left); Beamish Museum/Rev. J. Pattison (p.19 lower right, 26, 27 centre); David Bentley (p.24 lower); Laurie Campbell (p.31); Simon Danby (p.27 upper); Durham Wildlife Trust (p.36 right); Robert Hooper (front cover, p.13 left, 17, 24 upper, 29 right upper); David Jones (p.33 lower); Lunedale Heritage Group (p.7, 21 & 23 both lower right); John Nevin (p.11); Peggy Nixon (p.25 lower, back cover); Parkin Raine (inside front cover, title page, p.11, 14, 16, 19 upper, 20 upper, 21 upper right, 23 left & upper, 26 upper, 26 left, 29 bottom right, 38); Heiner Ruhe (p.13 right); Ernie Walton (p.28 right); John Wearmouth (inside back cover, p. 20 lower, 22). Joyce & David Wood (the Nixons, p.32).

All other photos: Rebecca Barrett or Neil Diment/NPAP.

Illustrations, quotes and loan of artefacts

Beamish Museum (p.8 & 35); Marcus Byron (p.7 & 9); Jane Carroll (hay time tea mug, p.25); Faber & Faber ('Ask the fellows' quote, p.6); Bill Heyes (p.8); Sarah Ingwerson (hay meadow flowers, p.3-5); Joint Nature Conservation Committee (JNCC – UK map, p.3); Mike Langman (p.17); Paul Rea (AONB map, p.2); Margaret Williams (clippers, p.11); Albert Weir (thrawcrook, p.35).

Inside rear cover:
Hay time at Stanhopegate, near Middleton-in- Teesdale, in the late 1930s.

Hay time tea, Lunedale. Look at those clogs!
(Could this be Carrie Raine, seen on p.14? If so, she has removed her white gloves for tea!)

He or she who is not old enough to have had their tea in a Teesdale hayfield just has not lived! Why did tea made half an hour earlier and kept in a galvanised can taste so good? The smell of hay with lots of plants other than grasses in it; scones with jam; gooseberry tart and rhubarb tart; the few bits of horse-drawn machinery standing silent... the reasons are endless.

Parkin Raine (Carrie's nephew)

The North Pennines AONB Partnership's Hay Time project is supported by Natural England via the Countdown 2010 Biodiversity Action Fund and the Heritage Lottery Fund (HLF).